Feb 8 1989.

TO: Jenny
"my no:2 Mum!"
A very happy Birthday.
Lotsa luv, Mary /88

WHEN THE CHIPS ARE DOWN WHO COOKS THE FISH?

JANUARY Monday 2nd

Oh God will it ever stop raining? Will I ever be able to replace Damian's "Leggo Nuclear Missile"? (accidentally trodden to death on Boxing Day.)

I've got a husband, two wonderful children and a beautiful house; for Christmas I received a matching set of copper saucepans, a year's subscription to "Good Housekeeping", and a Jane Fonda sweat suit. So I should be really satisfied... but I'm not.

<u>tonight</u> turkey croquettes and souffled mince pies - sourcream.

Emma helped me set the table, Damian refused, he said "Boys help Daddy wash the car". As ours fell to bits last month and Richard is saving up to replace it with a brand new Rover, he's on to a pretty safe bet.

BY VIV QUILLIN

ELM TREE BOOKS LONDON

Told Richard I felt suicidal, he said he was getting bored with me anyway, it was silly of me to expect him to listen, I could see he was reading the financial section. There was a time, years ago, when I admired his "dry sense of humour."

We met at the office party, he was so cool and witty, I was only a receptionist and very shy. He teased me about the way I accidentally disconnected him on transatlantic phone calls, called me "Helpless Heather", it was so sweet. He said I needed someone to take care of me and volunteered for the job. I've been waiting on him hand and foot ever since.

Sometimes I dream of a quiet office and me sitting behind a desk with a phone I can take off the hook, and a book of accounts to do. Numbers don't get over tired, they don't misbehave when you leave them for a minute. If you make a mistake you can find it and correct it, and at the end of the day you can make the figures come out right.

Families are a totally different matter. I thought raising children was going to be the most creative thing I'd ever done. I didn't think about getting no holidays, no pay and no notice taken of me.

Richard says I'm on holiday all the time Ho-Ho-Ho.

Richard says I've lost my sense of humour. It may be under the ironing... I shall hide my despair behind the Sunday supplements.

∗ Damian will have to wear one of Emma's nighties, I haven't got an inexhaustible of dry pyjamas.

Found fourteen "Stickee Chew" wrappers, five crisp bags, decayed banana and Action Man in a Sindy doll dress behind Damian's bed. How have they got there? He is only allowed raw carrot between meals, and is whoever put them there having a gender crisis? Have I failed somewhere, as a mother?

At least there is some good news, suddenly the Sunday papers have stopped advertising Habitrap furniture, de-luxe exercise bikes and bottle-pane double glazing - and are full of holidays.

That's just what I need to get over this silly depression, an escape from the endless round of feeding the masses, mucking out the bathroom, everything... except Emma's sinuses which will have to come with us.

Over the last few years Richard and I have grown a long way apart, I'm down here and he's up there. A romantic fortnight in the sun could re-ignite the spark, make him look at me as a woman, help me find the tender caring man he used to be.

...it'll be a second honeymoon - I'll get to know the girl I love...again...

* Will catch Richard between pub and late night violence on T.V. and talk to him nicely.

JANUARY Wednesday 18th

Richard and I have nothing in common anymore! I don't think a 'real ale' pub at the foot of Snowdonia is a good enough reason for spending a fortnight climbing it, quite apart from what the altitude would do to Emma's sinuses.

I got the feeling he was suggesting ridiculous ideas so he could say I was being unhelpful when I disagreed. Surely he wasn't serious about a fortnight's tour of Europe's night spots, bed unnecessary, breakfast on the coach and Damian* being sick every three miles?

I've never lost my temper before, Mummy used to say "a smiling faces moves mountains". I always try and be reasonable and understand the other person's point of view, but something inside snapped and I started screaming terribly negative things, though not loud enough to wake the children of course

I said I was terribly sorry afterwards, I know losing control is not the way for a mature adult to behave. Richard is still sulking, he got his haircut today and it looks hideous, just as it begins to get to a strokable length he goes and has another 'computer crop: Does he think a streamlined head makes his brain go faster?

* Richard's face, framed by the Hebrides, was unforgettable!

Both children had four fillings at the dentist this afternoon. I felt so ashamed, the dentist kept saying "Dear, Oh Dear mummy, this is disappointing." He's not what you'd call a children's man, I think for relaxation he pulls people's heads off without anaesthetic. I was rather glad Damian bit him...

Went to see the doctor last week, told him I felt very aimless and depressed and I was worried in case it had a detrimental effect on the children. He checked that my pulse was still going and my chest was in the usual place, and said lots of people would be glad to be as healthy as me. Perhaps I hadn't enough to do, why not get a hobby or have another baby?

I felt like a spoilt baby that's got lots of toys and is still discontented. I've got all the right ingredients to be happy, slim figure, fitted kitchen, wall to wall carpets and no financial worries. There was a miner's wife on "Women Chatter" at lunch time, she had practically nothing left in her house because the bailiffs had taken it all. But she possessed a kind of grim purpose that I envied....

Snap out of this self pity Heather! I'm going to clean the house from top to bottom, experiment with a new eye-shadow and try out a new recipe for tonight's meal!

<u>shopping</u> tooth paste, four pounds carrots, ingredients nut cutlet supreme.

FEBRUARY Monday 13th

Had coffee with my old chum Carole who I met at ante natal classes. She was the only one wearing shorts and a bikini top when we were both eight months pregnant. She's very loud and not my type really, but she does cheer me up...

Haven't dared broach holidays again with Richard, but Carole and Mike are going to Tenerife and leaving the children with her mother, if it was me I'd rip up my return ticket! Only joking of course, I wouldn't leave Emma and Damian like that, it could permanently damage them by my unconscious rejection. (I wonder if the psychologists who write about parenting ever look after their own children?)

I've been ironing for an hour and I've still got the Tea towels and Richard's vests and pants to do. Mike does all Carole's ironing for her, and her weekend shopping, I must admit he is a bit of a wimp, he lets Carole do whatever she wants.

Richard says unless men act like men and women act like women, one's never going to know where one is. So what happens in one parent families?

Actually got taken out by him last night, with his old chum Basher. I was assured there was no offence intended... — but why were all the merry quips at my expense?

FEBRUARY Tuesday 14th

Didn't expect one anyway.....

Emma has told her friend I could beat her mum up any day, I was naturally horrified and explained that mummies are gentle and caring and don't do that. She then offered to beat her up for me! I was quite taken aback, Emma is so timid at home, she's almost afraid of three year old Damian who is very high spirited and assertive. I suppose it's better that way round as Damy will have to stand up for himself when he's a man whereas it's somehow not very feminine for girls to do that.

When I take a grievance to Richard he always explains how unreasonable and illogical I'm being, which leaves me feeling a bit of a fool. If I could beat him in an argument I'm sure he'd sulk for days and I couldn't bear that. Caught him in a good mood last night and he agreed to a referee in further holiday summit talks, we are going to a travel agent on Saturday. He was quite enthusiastic!

Told Carole about it when we met outside school, she thinks I let Richard dictate to me, but as he says "You can only have one captain on a ship." Richard says his job is to hunt the meat and my job is to cook it. Richard says if I want to go out and earn a living he'd be glad to stay at home all day. ... there must be an answer to that one but I can never think of it.

3am. Woke up from dreadful nightmare about Captain Bligh and the mutiny on the Bounty. Didn't know whether the ship had a hole in it, or the sea was too rough, either way it was sinking. Woke to find Damy shouting someone tried to drown him in his bed. Changed sheets and wrung out mattress.

as captain of this house - I have the Divine Right
to say whats what

Whilst I pored over the travel brochures, Richard pored over the travel agent. I felt really humiliated. Apparently she plays backgammon in the Royal Corgi and he's already 'made her acquaintance.' Why does he only show his charming side to women he hasn't chosen for life? I suppose it's the male conquering instinct, the novelty of capturing me has worn off and he wants a new victim ...I mean...challenge.

The holiday in Crete he has booked is far more than we can afford but he obviously wants the travel agent to think he's some kind of business tycoon. Whilst I kicked his leg under the table (rule 1. a loyal wife never makes her husband look small in public) he leered expansively and signed everything in sight.

I don't resent her, she was very understanding about the children colouring in British Airways Summer Schedule. And didn't mind at all about Damian's wet patch on the chair, is his unreliable bladder a sign that he feels insecure? Oh Dear, not only am I a totally unappealing wife, I'm failing as a mother too.

Emma asked me why the radio psychologist is only interested in boys, I explained that he's talking about girls' development too, he just finds it inconvenient to mention both sexes.

"I don't know why, Emma, it always has been that way. I don't know why girls don't get a turn, now be quiet there's a good girl. . . . "

MARCH Friday 2nd

Damian scattered a jar of lentils yesterday, just after I'd vacuumed. I know he's just being lively so I mustn't get cross, but I could have STRANGLED him! If only he was reliably dry he could go to the playgroup or I could dump him on someone else for a while, but I won't let anyone know I can't even train my own child's bladder. All the other kids of his age stopped having accidents ages ago, except Carole's Timmy, (she's such a sloppy mother he doesn't count.) Carole reckons the other mums are lying about their children being dry at ten months, but I'm sure nobody would do that.

At least Carole is honest though she isn't at all tactful and can be quite rude. She interrupts Mike all the time, he doesn't seem to mind, Richard would have one of his compressed rages. I don't invite them over any more because Richard says she is vulgar and loud mouthed, it's true but she doesn't seem to care.

Oh God — you bore on something chronic, you really do

Have decided I don't really like socialising with Richard anyway, he always makes me look such a boring idiot. Carole says it's disgusting the way I fawn over him, she is mean, I just want to please him so he'll be nice to me. Mummy says a man's ego is very fragile and he needs to feel cleverer than his wife, after seven years of this game, my ego is lying bleeding on the ground like a squashed slug.

Spent this morning clearing out the loft for a jumble sale, I suppose my old "Girl's Crystal" annuals could go... I wanted to be a ballet dancer in those days, just until Mr Right came along of course. What a little mouse I was, waiting for a knight in shining armour to wake me with a grope and make me happy for ever – like the magazines say. I couldn't wait to get a husband and be somebody. And after the novelty of being Mrs Richard Aspic wore off, I became a mother, something he certainly couldn't do! He was very good about Emma not being a boy, I felt really clever when I produced Damian, well done Heather! Continuing the Aspic line....

So why do I feel like the Invisible Woman? People only know me as Mrs Aspic or Emma-and-Damian's-mum, it's as if I don't exist on my own behalf There must be more to me than this.

Told Richard I was having an identity crisis, he replied, "Don't be silly, you're my wife and the children's mother aren't you?" He suggested I take a couple of aspirins, and (while I'm in the kitchen anyway) make him a cup of tea.

Maybe I should do some further education, I used to be really good at maths when I was at school, but my friends called me "Brain Box" so I did A-level English instead.

If I'd known I'd wind up cleaning your armour every day, I'd never have let you rescue me in the first place

Richard has informed me that he's invited his mother to come on holiday with us. How could he, without asking me first? Because he knew I'd say no that's why.

Has he forgotten the fortnight we shared a caravan in kent? I know the weather wasn't her fault, or the children getting pneumonia the second week, but she never once stopped moaning. I do at least try and act as if I'm having a nice time.

I've never heard anyone go on so long about the pain she suffers but nobody knows because she doesn't complain. She's had so much taken out it's a wonder that there's anything left inside to go wrong. I know she's lonely on her own, but she never spoke to Richard's father when he was alive, anyway. I do feel bad about her and if she didn't make me feel so guilty for not being old and ill, I'd invite her over more often. I'd rather stay home than take that mobile funeral with us.

At least she's good for my figure, her spectre like presence at the dinner table takes my appetite right away. I've been indulging myself a bit lately and am ashamed to admit, I've gained 2½ pounds.

2am. Woke Richard and told him if she comes, I'm staying at home. He said "that's up to you Dear". I cried quietly into my pillow so as not to disturb him, then I cried really loudly and he still wouldn't wake up.

I hate dirty washing especially smelly socks screwed into little balls that have to be un picked. I hate automatic washing machines because people expect you to wash everything twice as often when it's NO trouble, and I hate Richard — No I don't, I know he's a good husband, but he doesn't seem to need me at all; Except to do the jobs nobody wants anyway. How can he calmly talk about going on holiday without me?

I don't know what to think anymore, I do get fed up with Damy always wrecking the place, but what would I fill the time with if he wasn't there? I thought the children would refuse to go without me and Richard would have to back down... but Emma says she's going to look after Daddy for me and Damian can only think about Granny Aspic's promise to show him her varicose veins.

Oh Heavens! Richard's conference shirts have all come out mauve! He'll think I did it on purpose because I'm upset. He says I'm unnecessarily overwrought and perhaps a quiet fortnight on my own would do the whole family good. But I'm very welcome to go with Deidre, the children and himself if I want to. I'd rather die than give in... but I'd be so scared on my own.

* what if there was a burglar?

* I don't even know how to set the alarm clock...

* I wonder if Prince Philip screws his socks into smelly little balls?

Whilst I was separating Damian from Emma's toast at breakfast yesterday, Richard said I'd better be quick making my mind up so he can change the holiday booking to five before it's too late. He was so confident that I wouldn't contemplate staying at home, I wanted to slap him. (I didn't of course.)

Last night I was watching television whilst Richard rearranged the government's strategy at the Royal Corgi. I couldn't help noticing the adverts, full of young women being blissfully happy in immaculate fitted kitchens, with clean, smiling children and tired Daddies coming home to be transformed into charming lovers, by being given the right meal and the whitest sheets. It makes me feel there is something wrong with my family because we aren't like that. But they are actors, paid to smile, and I'm out here in real, ordinary life.

I've been thinking what I could possibly do with myself if I decided not to go on holiday with the family, and there are lots of ways I can keep busy. . . .

: chuck a load of Emma + Damian's rubbish away without mass hysteria (till they get home.)

: wash the kitchen floor without Damy galloping all over it before it's dry.

: clean the bathroom and it would stay clean

: brush up my maths and enquire about classes, despite Richard saying standards have gone up and I'd never cope, (he always used to say exams were far stiffer when he was a boy.

: 12 p.m. read as late as I liked...

1 a.m. sleep undisturbed!

Last night was so embarrassing, I was pretending to be asleep, despite Richard shaking me and shouting sweet nothings down my ear, then Emma woke with a nightmare and I had to see to her and admit I was awake after all! Anyway, I can't avoid Richard's "attentions" indefinitely or the next thing I know, he'll be looking elsewhere. One can never relax, there are plenty of other girls ready to charm him.... if I'm not fun to be with.

Emma wants her hair cut because it hurts having the tangles combed out, I've persuaded her to keep it long because it's really her best feature. A girl can't learn too soon, her looks are her main asset. Mummy always said, " In the marriage market act small, sweet and silly and they'll be putty in your hands." Unfortunately this seems to wear off later, putty is not so easy to handle when you've got rubber gloves on and a bucket of dirty nappies to sort out. "No DAMIAN, leave them ALONE, you'll get cholera!"

Although I'm really worried that the family may manage all right without me, I'm going to stay at home... and enjoy it.

1. Get up really late
2. Read the papers with no interruptions from ANYONE!
3. Dance to stereo without people sneaking in and laughing
4. Look up some old friends and go for drinks
· · · Spotty Bell was strong on maths · · ·

* Two weeks doing exactly what I like, this could be the best holiday I've had in years!

Mothers Day came and went unrecorded except for a glass of diluted lemonade and a packet of crisps at 6:30 am from Emma . Richard says Mothering Sunday is politically unsound as mothers should be appreciated and respected all year round. Presumably he sent respects to his mother, I sent mine four carnations through Minta-Flora, it was all the housekeeping would stretch to .

If I spend "my housekeeping money" on other things, I always feel I'm taking food out of my family's mouths. I wish housewives got wages, just imagine time and a half for making tea or feeding babies after nine o'clock at night! Richard says women should look after their families for love not cash, and anyway his earnings belong to all of us: But he won't have a joint account and goes into a huff for days if I try to discuss it . I wish I didn't get so upset when he's in a mood, he doesn't even seem to notice if I sulk.

While the family were pigging their way through dinner tonight, I announced my intention to remain at home whilst his mother goes on holiday instead. In a quiet (but dignified) voice I said, "I can't stand in the way of an old lady's happiness, I hope you all have a wonderful time without me".

It was rather moving actually....

Richard was really distressed at the thought of leaving me behind, I'd no idea he would mind so much. In the end he offered me a hundred pounds to spend on myself if I go to Crete with them... and he'll tell his mother she can't come. (How can he tell his mother she can't come?)

I rather wish I hadn't agreed to it now, does Richard think money will buy everything? I feel like a prize in a competition that nobody has won. I don't think he's very happy about it either, though he says everything is fine...

Just started putting Emma's hair in bunches, it looks so sweet, she complains that the boys keep pulling them but I'm sure she'll get used to it in a few days. I do like making her look pretty, I wouldn't mind if she got dirty of course but she seems to want to stay clean anyway. Not like Damian, I must get his hair cut, it's full of knots and he makes a terrible fuss when I comb it.

Whilst I was enquiring about maths courses I found out some details on training as an accountant, which I've always fancied doing. I'd have to attatch myself to a firm of accountants and do my studying as well as working for them. I don't see how I could possibly manage... unless I had a wonderful little wife in the background.

It sometimes seems as if the whole world has set out to make it as difficult as possible for me to be anything but a mother, and that's not exactly a piece of cake either. I could fill my life with little hobbies I suppose but water-colour by numbers won't fill the empty hours between now and ninety.

Parents' evening at the school tonight, I insisted on Richard coming with me, "There is more to being a father than dishing out pocket money and filthy looks" I said to him.

Why do they always glare at the mother when they say rotten things about the kids? Apparently Emma is being really aggressive, particuarly with the little boys, she tied Jeremy's hair in bunches and filled it with plasticine; Aubrey Philips was found bound and gagged in the Wendy House after a two hour search round the school. I am amazed, she is so quiet at home and never gets cross when Damy breaks her toys because she knows he's only a baby.

Deidre (Richard's mother) baby sat whilst we were at the school and stayed for dinner, he has still not plucked up courage to tell her she is no longer included on the holiday. However, whilst toying with her lasagne (she doesn't trust Italians) she said quarantine for her budgerigar would be impossibly expensive and as Benjy is her only friend, she wouldn't go anywhere without him.

.... And anyway, she didn't want to spoil our holiday by coming along.

Who was it that gaveth with one hand and tooketh
away with the other?

Over the Easter weekend Damian ate four chocolate eggs of his own plus three belonging to Emma, in one afternoon. She was so good about it, never said a word. But yesterday when she accidentally put his "Blaster Tank" in the micro-wave, Damy had a terrible tantrum. That little boy is going to be just like his father (help!) ...And Emma is behaving just like me....!!!

Mummy and Daddy visited us on Bank Holiday Monday. Mummy is very supportive, thinks I do far too much and deserve better than this. Daddy says I'm like him, enjoy a bit of a challenge (it's the Bijou blood in me). He then went on to interrupt and contradict everybody right through tea. When they were leaving he told me in a loud confidential whisper that "Mummy is a bit tricky to handle, she's going through the CHANGE".

Why do women's moods always get put down to their wombs and yet men can be as sulky or bad tempered without even needing an excuse.

The Chancellor of the Family Exchequer informed me whilst brushing his teeth before bed, that unless we make severe cuts in our expenditure ie. no food for next month, he will be unable to provide me with the promised bonus incentive for the holiday. I'm so Furious I haven't even cried! He thinks he's got the better of me and he jolly well isn't going to get away with it. A promise was made and he's going to keep it if I have to go out and steal the money myself.

    ✳   Never noticed before what a SMUG face Richard has.

Carole dragged Damian and me down to the pub yesterday to work out a plan to raise the hundred pounds. After I rejecting her idea of robbing a bank, (she did offer to drive the getaway bicycle) or posing as a blind busker, she accused me of whinging and whining and never doing anything for myself. She is a pig, I don't know why I visit her at all.

Anyway I've done it! I marched into the bar and got myself a job five evenings a week at the Royal Corgi. At one stroke I've raised our income and lowered our expenditure. I'll earn one pound fifty an hour, and Richard will have to babysit, thus saving another one pound fifty an hour usually spent at the aforesaid Royal Corgi.

I'm a little over qualified with six "O" and two "A" levels, but it isn't easy to find work that fits with caring for small children, and its only until I've earned the money of course. . . . Richard's not very happy about it, I'd have thought he'd be glad that if he can't fulfil his promise I've found a way to do it for him. I hope he manages all right with the children, it would be funny if he turned out to be a better mother than me!

No it wouldn't.

* Had a note from school on Tuesday, Emma has formed a feminist group in the infant playground. They hiss at little boys and trip them up. Godfrey Morgan is refusing to attend school. (I thought he was the class bully?)

Sorry Darlings must fly!

Gosh what a whirl! After meeting Emma from school I've barely time to do my make up and throw some "Je t'aime" on, then it's off to the pub. Richard gives the children their tea and puts them to bed, he'll remember what their names are soon. I try to prepare the meal before I go, but there isn't much spare time when one is a career woman.

Richard is very moody at the moment, I thought he'd be pleased to see me being more out-going, he always admires other men's wives when they are independent. But then he also admires other men's wives when they flirt and wear low cut dresses.

I don't feel so desperate when he sulks nowadays, working at the pub there are lots of people who like and admire me so I'm not so dependent on Richard's opinion. If he's grumpy when I come home I just go to bed and leave him to it.

Richard's had the same nightmare three times this week. He builds a magnificent castle, then a woman from the council says it's got subsidence and it starts to crumble with him inside it.

He's never had nightmares before...

* <u>shopping</u> tights, hair rinse - red?

Got home from work to find Richard striding round grimly with his hands hovering at his hips, and talking out of the side of his mouth. As I suspected, he'd been watching another John Wayne re-run on T.V. He loves anything to do with cowboys, detective-cum-thugs, or spacefiction, then scoffs at me for reading escapist romances.

Not being able to afford a professional private detective, he is sending his mother to keep a frigidaire eye on me every evening at the pub. Her glare drops to sub-zero if I smile at anyone under fifty. Being friendly with customers is part of the job, at least that's what Richard told me when I thought he seemed rather intimate with one of the female staff. . .

Mike has run away with Carole's mother! He says he is fighting agism against women. I don't know how Carole can possibly manage without him, they are still paying for the rumpus room and he does more housework than her

My mother says any woman who allows a man to do her ironing deserves to be left. Richard wouldn't recognise an iron if it poked him in the eye ... does that mean I'm stuck with him forever?

Oh dear, that sounds dreadful, I do love him of course, I'm just not sure why.

Mrs Harrington informed me outside school that her daughter Cheryl had helped Emma and Louise form a protection racket for the smaller boys. She seemed quite proud of Cheryl. Emma just looked wide eyed, sweet and silent when I asked her about it.

I've hidden the tin opener and put the vegetable peeler in a prominent place. Emma and Damian love having hamburghers and oven chips every night but I'm sure convenience foods can't be as good for them as meals that need proper preparation. The kids think it's great fun having Daddy looking after them, they tell him how to do it.

Have put on eight pounds since I started work, Richard says I'm letting myself go, but the customers at the Royal Corgi think the extra weight suits me. Jane, one of the other barmaids, is getting married and has invited me on a hen party outing to "Nightbirds" discotheque, to celebrate her last night as a free woman.

I keep getting an urge to save her before it's too late ... marriage seems a terrible waste of such a lovely girl ... what am I saying?

That WOMAN was on the news tonight, why does Richard admire the way she runs her politics, like a steam roller running over everyone in her path, he hates women like that. Perhaps he doesn't see her as female because she's Primeminister. My mother thinks Mrs Thatcher is wonderful because she reminds her of the Queen.

* Will have to tell Richard it's a meal at a steak house, he'd never let me go to a disco on my own...

I did have a little talk with Jane, and she says she doesn't mind losing her independence, after all she doesn't want to go out to work forever (her job's pretty boring anyway): And if Tom's going to concentrate seriously on his career, someone's got to do all the little, necessary jobs for him, like cooking and washing shirts. "Mind you", she said, "if I'm going to sacrifice my job for him he'd better come up with the goods or there will be trouble!"

She was only joking of course . . .

Richard's mother came round for Sunday dirge - I mean dinner - today. After he'd settled down with the paper and I'd separated the children, she tottered into the kitchen to watch me wash up (she can't lift dishes since her last operation). To my surprise she pressed a ten pound note into my hand, to buy "one of those two piece bathing costumes they all wear nowadays". It was awfully sweet of her, even if I did get a three hour account of how she'd never gone in beyond her knees since Richard was born; For fear her loose ovary should shift and throw her off balance. Deidre has some extraordinary ideas about her internal organs, I suppose biology didn't get past the life cycle of the caterpillar when she was at school.

Emma and Damian played hysterectomies all afternoon, even Action man had one. Emma asked if Granny Aspic had pleats all over her tummy "like mummy's". Maybe I'm too old for a bikini?

Finally called on Carole yesterday, felt a bit awkward, I don't want her to think I'm visiting out of pity because her man has left her. Actually she was very cheerful and said men stink anyway. She is going round with a black feminist she met at Gingerbread. Celeste is very aggressive and calls women "sisters" and men "Finks."

In the mean time, Richard is complaining about unsociable hours, no pay and even less gratitude. He says I don't look up to him the way I used to. It's true, since he's done more around the house it's brought him down to my level some how. Yesterday he said in a very noble voice "I've cleaned the bathroom for you, and washed your plastic duck, it was filthy."

Where is it written that house work belongs to women? I don't remember Moses carving any stone memos about this, yet I do feel horribly guilty if someone else cleans the loo.

My husband is acting as though I'm going through a difficult phase and he's humouring me until I recover. In bed last night he suggested that perhaps what I need is another baby to help me settle down again.

I think he prefers me being dependent on him, and yet I always felt he rather looked down on me... Hmmm...

* Deidre has found out about the disco somehow! She says it's her duty to tell Richard unless I take her with me — to keep an eye on things. I've no choice, she'll have to come!

Went clothes shopping on Saturday, five year old boys will not be swimming in trunks this season as the shops haven't got any. Emma begged for black thigh boots — what has got into that child?

I couldn't get a thing to fit, having set out feeling comfortably rounded, within the space of two changing rooms I became an army tank. Is there a conspiracy to make women feel so ashamed of their size that they hide at home, thus covering up female unemployment figures? Carole reckons it's easier to find a bikini to fit a camel, than to find a job that pays enough to cover child care and make a decent living.

Bought Richard a super T-shirt, like a string vest with sleeves, it will look great with a tan showing through. He has lost over half a stone since I started work, and would be really good looking if his face wasn't so sullen.

When the children and I arrived home, he'd polished off a whole bottle of wine and we had a terrible row. He said he'd always worked hard to give me the best things in life and now that wasn't good enough for me, I earned my own money and didn't need him any more. He thinks I was "nice" to him in order that he would buy me a new washing machine or microwave oven, but it wasn't that way at all. I wanted him to be nice back to me... he cares for me with money instead of affection.

* Does "nice" mean smiling all the time and never disagreeing?

Dorothy Midgets
why are the shops full of size ten clothes, when the streets are packed with size fourteen women?
EMACIATED
TINY
small

I took Deidre to the hen party at "Nightbirds" on Friday evening, never again! My mother always said Richard's family weren't quite our sort and I know what she meant. Far from sitting quietly in a corner, Mrs Aspic Seniour had to be forcibly removed by the bouncers after doing the Black Bottom whilst stripping to her vest and directoires.

She then led the whole discotheque plus D.J in a conga round the police station next door. She's got a date with the constable who booked her and wants to know when we are going again... I may never recover...

The whole town has been wallpapered overnight in peace posters about Greenham Common, they are in rainbow colours and made me feel very uplifted somehow. I do think the media is unfair, going on about them looking unkempt, they don't report if the miners have shaved or pressed their trousers when they are picketing. Anyway, when men were in the trenches in wartime it was a mark of their heroism that they put up with those conditions.

I think the press can't bear seeing women being just as brave so they pretend peace mongers like living in squalor. Richard says we should get the army out to deal with irresponsible peace demonstrators, I thought we already had done...

* Richard wants to know if I've got my hundred pounds together yet, but with all my expenses ie. work clothes, convenience foods...it's very hard to save really....

I've got to take the string T-shirt back, Modesty Aspic says it is not his habit to display everything he's got and his body is being saved for the intimacy of the marriage bed. He also said my new bikini was obscene, I presume he was talking about the body more or less inside it. where is it written that fully grown women should look like twelve year old girls?

After snarling at the whole family for days, Richard has finally admitted that there are going to be some redundancies at Speed Rat Computers ... and he's worried about his job. I can't think why, from what he's told me he practically runs the place, they couldn't possibly manage without him. He wouldn't discuss it any further, I can only judge from the continuing snarls that he is not o.k.

It is very difficult trying to comfort someone who is being really bad tempered and won't admit there is anything wrong. Yet when I cried last night because, just as I thought Damian had improved, I found another puddle (by sitting in it at 11.45pm) — Richard pretended not to notice.

11.59.   Richard says when he does try to cheer me up I immediately get a headache and want to go to sleep. Humphhh!

Dreamt I had never left work and I was now Personal Assistant to the Managing Director. I had a beautiful house full of Siamese cats. Richard kept popping up all over the place, first he was a cleaning lady, then a nanny in the park, then serving in the launderette and finally a cordon-bleu chef, hired for one of my dinner parties. He must have been exhausted by the end of the dream . . . .

Richard is always moaning that I'm not interested in sex and he has to make all the effort, but the odd time I do get the urge, he picks a quarrel with me or says he's got a very busy day tomorrow and has to conserve his energy. I started unbuttoning his pyjama jacket on wednesday night and he screamed that I was sex mad; how come when he unbuttons my nighty its because he's sex starved?

It's all over between Deidre and her police constable and she wants to know when we are going back to "Nightbirds" to get another. She's bought a jumpsuit, dyed her eyebrows and painted Benjy's toe nails silver. She made her entrance on one of my rare evenings at home. The kids and I openly gawped and Emma screamed " Granny! You look like a prehistoric rock star!" But Richard's face never moved a muscle. That man watched too many Marlon Brando movies at an impressionable age, one can never tell what he's thinking:

Which makes it very difficult when he expects me to know how he feels without him telling me anything. It's almost like babies and mothers. . .

Nowadays I feel like a little boat without an anchor, I hadn't realised, until I stopped believing that Richard somehow always knew best, how very safe that used to be.

Cwums!
Crikey!
G-G-Gosh...
Keep a stiff upper lip... my own Mother!... has she no Self Respect!... My GOD... what does she LOOK LIKE!

Bumped into Cheryl Harrington's mum outside school this morning, she tells me my daughter is running a girls only self defence class in the lunch hour. Mrs Harrington says Cheryl is twice the child she used to be and would I let her know if Emma is planning an adult class? My little girl is leading a double life!

It's suddenly occurred to me, I wasn't taught to stand up for myself, I was trained to find someone else to do it for me ie. Richard... no wonder I'm not very good at it when I find I need to stand up to him most of all....

Deidre and I went for lunch at Jane's Neo Georgian town flat on Monday. It is exquisite, everything is white without fingerprints. She's just come back from her honeymoon in Israel, it reminded me of Richard and I starting out together, we weren't speaking by day three either.... Deidre helpfully pointed out it takes you twenty or thirty years to get used to each other by which time one of you dies anyway. Jane has given her the phone number of a retired police sergeant she knows.

I ought to ring my mother, she doesn't approve of my new job and is full of sympathy for poor Richard. It seem she only supports me if I'm as down trodden as she is. He thinks if I stop work everything will get back to normal, but it won't. I've grown up.

If only Richard would stop burying his head in the sand, we might be able to talk about the awful rift between us. Oh Dear.....

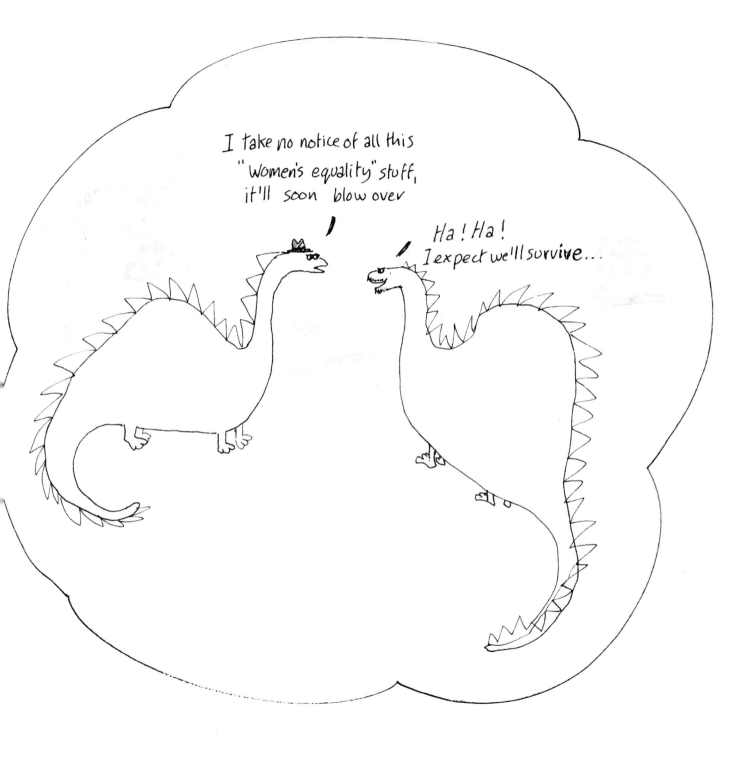

Emma broke up for the summer holidays last week, and I did some detective work : On Tuesday she had Cheryl and Julie over to play so I crept down the garden and caught them having an assault course under the strawberry nets. When I confronted Emma she insisted they were playing hide and seek - with back packs and spiked boots?

Deidre took Damian ice skating with the Over Sixties Limbo Dancing Circle, she can hardly walk today but says she's prepared to pay for her pleasure. I can't wait to get old so I can do what I like too. She certainly tired Damian out, most of the time I've barely pulled him out of one mass of destruction before he's into the next. I caught myself at 8.30   this morning thinking, only nine and a half hours to go before it's Richard's turn.

This afternoon we went over to carole's, from what I could hear above our combined kids fighting, she is just about coping without Mike. She has taken in two students to help with the bills, they also help with the housework and children. Mike has the kids at weekends while she goes to a Women's Rage group with Celeste. She has found out that married women have twice as much mental and physical illness as those who are single.

Celeste is campaigning for men to have a government health warning stamped on their foreheads. She asked me how I can sleep at night with the enemy so close at hand. I do think she is rather extreme, I like men, other people's husbands are often very nice to me.

AUGUST Friday 10th

Richard says I don't care about pleasing him any more, so I started a diet on Monday, two crispbreads a day and as many elderberries as one can eat. Apart from blinding headaches and some dizzy spells it's going fine. Also converted my legs to the sort men love to handle. It's not true that waxing doesn't hurt! I'd sooner run Damian's birthday party without any aspirin. After peeling a two inch strip off my left ankle I couldn't bring myself to do any more ... went to the Royal Corgi in a summer frock and leg warmers. Richard pulled the rest off for me last night, I've a nasty feeling he enjoyed it.

My legs look like plucked chickens and I've gained two pounds seven ounces. It's really hard work trying to look right. I've spent ages this week getting my hair done, manicuring my nails, doing my make up carefully, all so Richard can laugh about how frivolous I am. Men are lucky, they don't have to worry about their appearance.

At least Richard did seem touched by my efforts, he hugged me and said I was a funny little thing. I felt happier than I have in ages, I do want to please Richard .... but I want him to please me too...

is the tie **too** formal?.. this one matches my cords... but the jeans make me look **taller**... Gray suit? Don't want to **look** as if I've tried too **hard**... but it **is** a first date ... **perhaps** the...

He is being very affectionate and keeps saying, "Only a few days left of you working at the pub." I shall miss the Royal

I'm sure it's gone thinner at the back

Corgi gang, and Carole and Celeste, while I'm on holiday, but they'll all be here when I get home again.

AUGUST Friday 17th

you can't have anything to wear — it's all clean and packed!

Only a week until we go away and Richard has come home with some really bad news. Simon, who began work at Speed Rat Computers just after Richard, has been made redundant. Richard is very upset for Simon, but doesn't know if this means he himself is spared — or next on the list. He has brought home tons of work in order to prove himself more cost effective than a computer. But machines don't need to rest....

Strangely, I don't seem to be nearly as worried as him about how we would manage if he lost his job. I pointed out that we could move to a smaller house and even if we were very poor we would still have each other. He said quite crossly "That's not the point, a man should look after his family properly", and stamped out to the garage. He seems to think he's only valuable in terms of money.

Carole and Celeste took me to a miners' benefit earlier in the week, some of the miners' wives came and their version of the strike was quite different to what I'd seen on television and in the papers. We saw a video of some picket lines, I'd no idea we had so many police in this country. If it had been filmed in Poland and they'd had army uniforms on, it would have been described by our media as "state oppression".

I feel even if I listen to the news, I'm not being given a full picture of what's going on around me. But we're not in Russia, this is a free country, isn't it?

Damian is not taking his Lego Polaris submarine on holiday and that is final! Why do little boys want to play at war all the time? I suppose they are practising to be men. I had a really good idea this morning, if men fought wars with toy weapons instead of real ones, we could spend the billions of pounds saved-on wages for housewives. I wish I could solve Richard and me's problems as easily as the world's.

Usually I can only guess at his feelings as the granite exterior gets even harder when he's upset. But tonight I got home early and found him weeping in the garage. I've never seen him cry before, but at least he has finally admitted how frightened he is. He says he was brought up to work and couldn't survive without it. He says without a job he'd be nobody; I know the feeling.

He's always told me that if I wanted to go out and earn a living, he would love to stay at home with the children so I suggested that he could really do it now, enabling me to train as an accountant. It would involve me travelling away a lot and spending long hours at the office, but after four of five years I would be well able to support us all.

He said it was out of the question for him to stay at home with the kids, he did hope to retain some self respect. Why do men keep saying bringing up children is a valuable and important job and yet hardly any of them do it?

Apparently it's the right work for women but men have better things to do.... "Damian, don't disturb Daddy, he's BUSY, come and help me pack some more things for the holiday...."

Now **there's** a mother worthy of respect

Well, the father is God y'know...

of course it's not like being an architect or a doctor, you don't need training for motherhood, — any fool can do it

CAREERS OFFICER

there are no wages, holidays, promotions, pensions, but then, it's not a **proper** job is it?

although women are perfectly equipped to grow babies, we have spent undisclosed amounts of money, time and brain power, building babies in test tubes

...aren't we **brilliant**!

could it be anything to do with CREATION ENVY?

Finally arrived in Crete, despite seven hour departure delay and Emma being air sick twice before we left the runway. The hotel is very comfortable which is just as well as we had to stay in all morning. After lunch the rain had more or less cleared so we went out to explore. Emma is sulking because I didn't bring her umbrella and wellies.

Richard has resolved not to think about work until we get home. He immersed himself in the holiday spirit by drinking a great deal of ouzo before dinner and then fell asleep on my shoulder during the moussaka. There was a lovely couple at the next table, totally engrossed in each other (I bet they aren't married) with a dear little girl called "Peace."

Just to complete the atmosphere, one of the locals strolled round the restaurant playing the bouzouki, I know it sounds corny but when he looked into my eyes I felt he'd seen my soul. There were butterflies in my stomach but this could be due to the foreign water.

* My "Dire Trouble" tummy tablets don't seem to be helping at all...
* Wish Damian could tell the difference between the bidet and the loo.
* Weather is due to pick up soon.

Damy, Mummy's in rather a **hurry**...
could you wash action man's hair **another** time?
are you listening?
Falkland crisis
Grimm Fairy tale

Felix, Topaz and Peace were on the beach today and we got chatting; Topaz is half Malaysian and half West Indian which explains her rich, even tan and high cheek bones. My family are all faded pink all year, and not a cheek bone between them. Felix played with the little girl all morning (he makes much better sand castles than Richard.) Topaz never lifted a finger except to eat the icecream he bought her. I could get very interested in a man who plied me with icecream, on the other hand, if it was Richard I'd know what he was after...

Richard seems to think a holiday means only one thing, but I want a rest from the day to day chores, and that includes the night ones too. I'm not frigid but neither am I roused to passion by remarks like "Come on Heather, be a sport, don't you want me to have a good time?" And all the time he's chatting me up, I know he'll flounce off in a sulk if I say no, he's not really interested in sex being something we both share, he just wants to make sure he gets his own way. If he doesn't get instant submission from me, he seems to feel his testicles will explode. I don't see that he's going to come to any harm, monks manage all right, though they do seem to go bald...

Damian, Emma and Peace are getting on like a house on fire, they agree what to play by collective voting, Damian is constantly out voted so either does what the girls want or plays on his own.

.... Must go back to the hotel and lie down, Galloping Gut Rot is gathering speed and my English Rose complexion has turned tomato red.

Already a week has whizzed by! Richard obviously finds Topaz very attractive and has finally realised that his Gorilla strut is not impressing her, in fact she takes no notice of him except when he's playing with the children. Yesterday they all went to the children's entertainment and Felix and I stayed by the pool.

We had a really meaningful discussion, he's so understanding it was like talking to another woman. I've never talked about myself so much to a man before. (I've never found one that would listen that long) I could find him very attractive if he was a bit taller and looked more self assured.

Felix seems to assume we will take the boat trip to the nudist beach with them tomorrow, and I'm secretly dreading it. I know it's terribly good for the children to see people's bodies in their natural condition, but mine is in such bad condition, unless I'm wearing garments that push everything upwards and inwards, I tend to hide it under a towel. Topaz says we are all beautiful in our own way but she teaches jog, tap and boogying on down somewhere in London, and has the kind of body you see in adverts for still being able to ski/mud wrestle at 'that time of the month' in a skin tight outfit.

She and Felix share the child care as he finishes work by early afternoon and they spend a couple of hours developing their relationship before she leaves to take her evening class. Felix says making this planet more beautiful by clearing people's rubbish up, is one of the most internally purifying occupations he's ever had... I never thought of Dustmen that way before....

My top layer of skin has totally peeled off leaving me the colour I was originally - underneath.

Emma and Damian couldn't believe their eyes at the nudist beach, between Richard saving his body for the privacy of the marriage bed and me not wanting anyone to see how badly I compare with a normal woman, bare adults have been rather a closed book to my children.

But it was GREAT! There were people there of every shape and size, it was so nice, us all being different. Richard thought he was getting a cold and would have to leave his trunks on, he did take them off eventually - after doing a mental measurement with every other male on the beach. He insisted on putting the windbreak round me in case my more delicate regions got over exposed.... to the sun...

That night we both felt like it at the same time and couldn't do a thing, due to severe sun burn on bits which have been under exposed for the last thirty years. If I didn't feel I ought to fancy Richard, I could find him quite attractive at times...

We fly back to England on Sunday, so bought going home presents at a quaint local market this morning. It had everything you could buy in Camden only twice as expensive and covered in flies. Richard bought his mother a hand crocheted wool shawl in gray, I bought her a T.shirt with "Frankie goes to the Woolwich" across the front in lime green.

Tomorrow is our last night. We are all going to a night club in Rethimnon, I wish Richard would keep his lust for Topaz a little less obvious. I don't know whether I feel better or worse, seeing her make it quite clear that she wouldn't touch him with a barge pole.

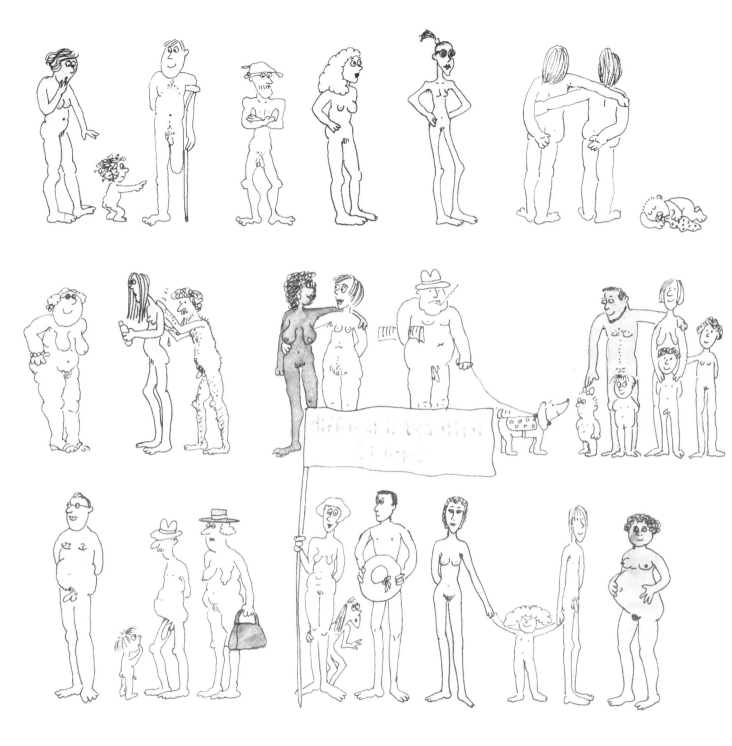

6.30 am.   We only just made it to the plane, Richard's eye is still swelling though his lip has stopped bleeding. The whole family is asleep so I can collect my thoughts at last.

All was going as well as could be expected in a nightclub crammed with sweating tourists, six Greek dancers smashing plates and a bouzouki orchestra. Then Topaz got bored and drifted out to the patio, Richard followed her for a breath of fresh air and then — TOTAL HUMILIATION.

Everybody heard him bellowing, "You'll be putty in my hands after I've tamed you", followed by a scream and a heavy thud. By the time fifty or so people had reached the patio, Topaz had thrown him over her shoulder and was sitting on his head with his arm in a double wrist lock.

Felix apologised to me because Topaz had settled a dispute with brute force. Topaz apologised to me for ripping   Richard's new hand woven shirt.

Richard apologised to me, said he learned his lesson and wanted his little harem girl back again. HAREM GIRL!
GRRRR!

Everyone made friends and exchanged addresses and Felix and Topaz said we must keep in touch, but I know they won't.

I feel as if nothing will ever be the same again.

North Ruislip appears to be more or less as we left it, (slightly less as supermarket and boutique closed and job centre pulled down.). Emma's heat rash has gone and so has my sun tan, it's in little flakes all over my side of the bed actually.

Deidre was delighted to see us, she has bought some purple lamé pedal pushers and sprayed Benjy to match - ready for our next night out. Oh dear, I don't really like Nightbirds that much, it's full of aging Peter Pans and school girls, I also feel horrible deceiving Richard, but Deidre has set her heart on it so I'll take her one last time.

Not that things could get any worse between Richard and I, he assumed I would give up my job after the holiday, and is furious that I haven't done. It was just temporary, to earn the holiday money, but I can't go back to being at home all the time. At the pub they treat me like a real person with a mind, not just a faceless skivvy. And I like being with the children much more when it's not my turn to look after them, twenty four hours a day.

I've tried to explain how I feel to Richard but he just bellows that I'm being hysterical and unreasonable and stamps off. I used to feel it was the end of the world if Richard was displeased with me, I suppose he WAS my world. I can't go back to pussy footing round his likes and dislikes, I'm not his shadow, I'm ME...whoever that is... "No Damian! I've just washed those, don't put them down the"...

it fits beautifully darling

SEPTEMBER Friday 21st

Deidre babysat earlier in the week on my night off and Richard took me out for a meal. For the first time I felt he was prepared to talk instead of trying to browbeat me into submission. He told me of his growing anxiety about the state of our marriage over the martinis, we covered the potential damage to the children due to my reluctance to be a full time mother through the avocados. During the beef bourgignon we discussed the way he has always taken his responsibilities seriously and how disappointed he felt that I no longer put the needs of the family first.

He has sat quietly at home with our children night after night hoping I would come back to them. I felt so greedy and selfish... I can't enjoy myself at other people's expense, I'll have to hand in my notice at the pub. I do want to be a good mother .... but what about me?

When we got home they were still up, Deidre was teaching Emma limbo-dancing and Damian was trying on the purple lamé pedal pushers.

Today it's raining so hard I can't even go and see Carole. When is it going to be my turn? When I'm forty and the kids have grown up... I can get a little part time job, nothing too interesting or well paid (I've no qualifications except motherhood and A-levels) Meanwhile Richard intends to avoid all the housework and childcare. I don't believe he thinks mothering is a valuable job at all... he just wants me to think so... so I'll keep on doing it. I've been had!

✳ tomorrow evening I take Deidre to Nightbirds for the very last time.

Of all the hypocritical, deceitful, lying toads! Who should I see body popping at Nightbirds but RICHARD. It turns out he was paying a baby sitter on Saturday nights and sneaking home just before me. I don't know who is more furious with whom.

From now on it's open war fare, Richard showed his true colours and said it's either the Royal Corgi — or him. I'll think it over... if I could get a wage rise and put a student in the loft, we might just get by without him. ... is this really happening?

I've tried not to worry the children but it's obvious that things are seriously wrong between us. Damian asked, if Daddy leaves could he be in charge and boss me around instead. Emma says I can go to her self defence class and learn to take care of myself.

Have checked around and discovered the Royal Corgi pays the lowest wages in the district, so got the girls together and we all went to see Maurice the manager. He said he'd love to pay us more but times are hard, he couldn't stay to chat as he was off for a game of golf. He wouldn't have talked to a man like that. Patronising creep!

There is a barmaids meeting in the Ladies, at 9 o'clock tonight.....

All the customers at the Royal Corgi have signed a petition in support of our wage claim. They will withdraw their thirst for an indefinite period if our demands are not met within a week.

I've been in a complete turmoil, not really knowing what to do, until Mummy invited me out for lunch. It wasn't anybody's birthday and I never usually see her without Daddy so I was quite surprised, Damian wrestled with the spaghetti bolognese and she wrestled with a carefully prepared talk on erring wives. She says it's the woman's job to make a marriage run smoothly because men aren't very good at that sort of thing. They are like little boys and need to be petted and spoiled all the time. She stays quiet and lets Daddy think he knows best because it keeps him happy.

As she brought me up, she feels responsible when I don't behave as a wife should. There was a long silence (apart from Damian chomping) we sat, festooned in bits of spaghetti, staring at the tablecloth. Finally I knew what to do. I hugged her and told her she had made everything clear for me...I don't want a marriage where I have to be like her — both mother and child but never equal partners. I felt very calm and strong, picking fronds of spaghetti off Mummy and Damian, I settled the bill and we left the restaurant. I put my mother in a taxi, Damy said Granny Bijou's mouth was so wide open you could see all the fillings at the back.

We just made it to the school gates before Emma came out. I feel ten years younger all of a sudden.

Barmaids Triumph In Battle Of The Beer! (spent my first wage rise in celebratory drinks for customers). Maurice said he was only joking when he refused more money at the start. Hmmph. This means I could just manage to get by without Richard (as long as he paid the mortgage and rates.)

We are finally speaking again as communicating through the children was inflaming the situation, Damian would make an excellent divorce solicitor. I told Richard that I've changed and if he doesn't want an equal partner he'll have to look elsewhere. Maybe some teenage innocent will take him on, but one day she'll grow up and he'll be faced with the same problem again. Richard says he's got to be head of the household or he can't hold his head - or anything else - up, again. He said he'd even permit me to work at the Royal Corgi if I let him be in charge of us.

We have agreed to pretend he is the boss, in order to hold the remains of his crumbling pride together. Dear Richard, I like him so much better when he acts like a vulnerable person with feelings instead of a lump of granite.

Even so, it's made me realise that if he had decided to go, without his financial help the children and I would be horribly poor. I don't think I'm qualified to do any job that wouldn't cost nearly as much in child minders, as I was able to earn. I haven't liked to pry into Carole's financial position, but they do all look rather down at heel. . . .

✳ Have finally allowed Emma to have her haircut, she says it gets in the way when she's weight training.

Richard is no longer a reluctant parent, having decided if you can't beat 'em, join 'em he is now In Charge Of Evening Parenting, and tells me to "Run along and have a nice time at the pub".

He's got loads of books out of the library on nutrition and household management, apparently there is a critical balance between food being over or under cooked, and for years I've been doing it the wrong way. I can't see that it's so crucial, we are all very healthy, but I didn't like to say this. He is going to prepare me some study work _for_ my evenings off. Emma and Damian now have an evening schedule which includes twelve and a half minutes jogging round the garden (two minutes intense aerobic activity), lessons in brushing their teeth the correct way, and fifteen minutes socially related discussion before bed.

We have a new book on "Creative Foreplay, A Step By Step Guide", which we are working through very slowly as most nights he is too engrossed in plotting charts of the children's growth and potential ability. We did the section on Body Massage last night, but I'm sure he turned two pages at once because we seemed to skip some quite large areas.

I am being very supportive, I say "Yes Richard" and "What a wonderful idea", and "Why ever didn't I think of that?" all the time. I don't want to go back to the way things were, but I do miss the familiarity of it.

Carole rang when I was out and apparently he gave her a lot of advice on washing powders. She told him to go and get fluff dried which was rather unkind. . . .

Daddy has been staying with us for a few days as he's rather shaken up. Leaving only a brief note, Mummy has gone to a retreat somewhere with Deidre, she wrote that she needed time to "rethink her lifestyle". Poor Daddy doesn't know how to do anything for himself, only how to tell other people what to do. He told me his marriage has been a great disappointment, he'd fallen in love with my mother because she was such a high spirited extrovert (MUMMY?!!) and she'd become a mouse who wanted him to think for her. He'd had an affair for years with a librarian who'd given him the scintillating companionship he needed, he'd never left Mummy because he knew she'd be helpless without him.

What a waste, he's squashed out of my mother the very things he most wants, why did he do that? Why did she let him? He really wants my mother now she's got up and gone, but will she come back? And if she does, can she keep standing up to him?

Emma has put on eight pounds recently, I'm sure it's due to her weight training. Richard says there are men in his office who don't even know how old their children are, let alone how much they weigh. The doorman swears by porridge oats, his kids are all over six foot tall. I pointed out to Richard that height is not everything and he said, "Leave this to me please Heather, I do know best."

It's not easy pretending he's the boss. . . .

Mummy has gone back home! She's bought a parrot which says "Shut up Terence Dear," every time my father speaks. Daddy is being fearfully polite to everybody, so far so good?

As I was working on Bonfire night, Richard took the kids to a firework display, he said their little faces were radiant, he wouldn't have missed it for anything, I wish I'd been there, it made me think what a lot of irreplaceable moments are missed by fathers working late or being away when their children are small. Do men decide to concentrate on their careers at that time, for the good of the family – or to escape from it?

This morning whilst I was doing the washing with Damian "haunting" me from under a pile of dirty sheets, Celeste turned up with a petition for some sort of women's centre. It is to have self defence classes and discussion groups on how women's work is devalued. "Honestly Celeste," I said, "You make us sound like second class citizens." She said I am a second class citizen, she is third class by being black as well as female.

Deidre is going to babysit tomorrow night whilst I go to a meeting on further education for women with Carole and Celeste, Richard is going to the Royal Corgi with his chums to reorganise the world. Last night we did the section on "Acting Out Our Fantasies." for Richard's I was a slave compelled to obey his every wish. When it was my turn I wanted him to be a fierce pirate, worshipping me in helpless adoration, starting at my toes . . . . he said it was very late and we'd do it next time.

I've set the alarm for 6.a.m. . . . .

Gosh it's not that long till Christmas, I must find time to buy some presents. It's difficult to shop with Damian, I've always got to hold onto him in case he gets lost, and go to the ladies in every store, (usually on the fifth floor.) I think Richard used to feel my days were an endless stretch of leisure, so if he asked me to pick up his cleaning or phone the garage, it gave me something to do. He now knows one can't do anything for more than ten minutes without interruption from Damy, or more important, finding out why he is quiet.

It might be easier after Christmas when he starts playgroup. He still leaves the odd pool around, but when I courageously mentioned it the supervisor airily said "Oh tons of them do that".

At the meeting on further education for women, I was the only one in high heels and lipstick. I resent women with lawn mower haircuts and washed out sweaters giving me patronising looks. The only course in our area which provides a crêche is a six week session called "Coping With Obsolescence When The Family Grows Up." Any woman attempting three or four years training, plus looking after her kids, would have to be off her head or desperate. Married men have got it so easy, a little wife to care for their children and themselves. It's NOT FAIR!

Celeste was very scathing about my naivety, she's been campaigning for equal rights for years, well she's got the time, she hasn't any children. She says, "Any man who won't share the child care equally should be shot, they are all war mongering bastards anyway."

Had a quiet evening at home with the kids last night, I gave them tea and put them to bed myself, it's so nice to do that occasionally. Richard and his mother went to Night birds but came home early. There was some sort of argument as Richard insisted on correcting his mother's body popping technique, Deidre said she'd learnt it at the Pineapple Studio so she ought to know best. He's got a black eye, she's broken her hand bag strap and they both got thrown out by the bouncers.

After last week's educational meeting I went out and bought some dungarees. One can buy them in really large sizes, there are lots of big feminists, have they given up trying to be petite size tens and got political instead? ... Or did they get to be feminist first and then didn't care about trying to be size tens any more? The dungarees are very roomy (even with Damian and his friend inside), I'm not sure if I really like them, but I thought Celeste would be pleased to see me making an effort.

I met her having baked beans on toast with Carole when Damy and I went round. Carole was really cross about my dungarees, said it was just as stupid dressing to please Celeste as dressing to please Richard. Why didn't I wear what I wanted? I'm not sure if I even know what I'd like to wear.

Celeste was very quiet, she's just discovered her girl friend is pregnant, and it obviously isn't Celeste's baby. She looked so unhappy I wanted to hug her but felt a bit nervous in case she took it the wrong way.... so I didn't.

I suppose I am a feminist but the uniform isn't really my taste

Topaz and Felix rang last night! I didn't think we'd ever hear from them again. They plan to spend Christmas meditating in a tent on the Pennine Way and would like to hitch hike down to see us at New Year. Their lives seem so carefree and exciting. I felt quite dull and drab when they rang off.

Suddenly I had a brilliant idea, Richard, Deidre, kids and self could dash off to ski in Austria at Christmas. Deidre was all for it (she was round at our house having an extra panel pinned into her wet look leotard when the phone rang). The big snag is, Richard doesn't want to go, he hates snow and wants Christmas in the comfort of his own home.

Deidre suggested we "leave the miserable, old bugger behind", she said from a baby he'd never been anything but trouble. She'd always wanted a girl for company, and boys are such hard, selfish thugs. I can't help thinking if she'd brought him up differently, he wouldn't be having quite so many problems now.

I can't go off skiing without Richard, much though I'd love to. He'd be so hurt, and anyway Christmas is a time when the family should be having a lovely time together.... Damian — that's the last time I'm TELLING YOU! * * !

I have just smacked my son's bottom, he must learn to have respect for other people's property, that includes Emma's book on mud wrestling ... and my shins.

DECEMBER Wednesday 12th

I'm rushed off my feet at the pub at the moment, Maureen is off with flu and Jane is off because Tom's got flu and she's looking after him.

Felt rather miffed that Richard seemed to take it totally for granted that if he didn't go skiing, I wouldn't go either. Perhaps he knows it was a sacrifice on my part, but can't say so. I do try and make allowances for his difficulty in showing emotions (like gratitude).

Deidre is taking lessons on a dry ski slope, she is going to a Russian all night movie with her instructor tomorrow. Emma was really keen to go away for Christmas with her grandmother but I felt she should be here with us. She muttered something about "It had better be good then," that little girl has changed a lot from the timid, shy mouse I once knew. I asked Mummy and Daddy if they wanted to join us on Christmas Day but they are going to a hotel in Brighton for a few days so Mummy can have a rest from cooking. Daddy doesn't actually help at home, but he does buy a lot of take away meals nowadays. . . and parrot seed.

I've been invited to spend Boxing Day with Carole and Celeste and various separated husbands and girl friends. Richard can come if he wants to, but I'm going anyway! He says my friends are a bad influence on me and fill my head with the wrong ideas. I pointed out that I am not Sindy Doll, to be programmed into feeling or behaving the way Richard - or anyone else - wants.

I am, odd though it may seem, perfectly capable of making my own mind up, he said there was no need for me to get "uppity."

For the first time in living history, Richard has done the Christmas shopping! I am in bed with flu and he has taken time off, from the great god - Speed Rat Computers, to take care of the family. He arranged to leave Damian with Carole (cheating, I thought) and spent one afternoon buying the presents I usually take a month to choose. All the relatives are getting the same thing for Christmas, why didn't I think of this before? I do hope they all like medium size brown mittens....

He and the kids are being unbearably smug and secret about what they have bought each other and me. If that man isn't careful, he'll soon be as fond of the children as I am.

Life is much happier now that I feel if our marriage seemed really hopeless, I could (just about) live independently of Richard. Celeste says, THEY (men) have designed the system so that women can't manage without men's financial help. Women who do leave their husbands must be heroically brave, truly desperate, or have a new meal ticket that wants them. It can't be good for either partner, living with such unequal powers. I'm sure it's better for Richard, as well as me, knowing I want to live with him .... rather than HAVE to.

There are strong burning smells wafting up from the kitchen, he is making cranberry jelly for Christmas. I am trying not to feel inadequate because I have always bought ready made cranberry sauce. I am also trying to wish it a success, but secretly hoping it tastes as vile as it smells.

I'm only human.

Deidre departed for Austria yesterday in a flurry of salopettes, moon boots and snow goggles, everybody else boarding the plane was wearing ordinary clothes. *Emma* is stomping round the kitchen with tennis racquets strapped to her feet, gripping rolled umbrellas for ski sticks.

I still feel rather wobbly, probably due to all the prune juice Richard insisted that I drank, he went back to work on Monday and is at the office party tonight. I'm trying not to remember all the stories he's told me about what "the other chaps" get up to. Have just decided to have a housewives Christmas party next year, we can all invite our milkmen, postmen, dustmen etc. and Richard can wonder what I'm getting up to.

It's midnight and still no sign of him, I've filled the stockings and wrapped the tea set I bought for Damian. It's never too early to learn how to make a cup of tea.

What a lot of changes there have been in our family since last Christmas. Richard does share in the family a lot more now, but I do wish we didn't have to act as if it was a personal favour on his part. And I double wish he didn't have to be best at everything in order to survive.

1 am. If there's a trace of perfume on him when he comes in, the wok I bought him with a thousand uses will have one more added......

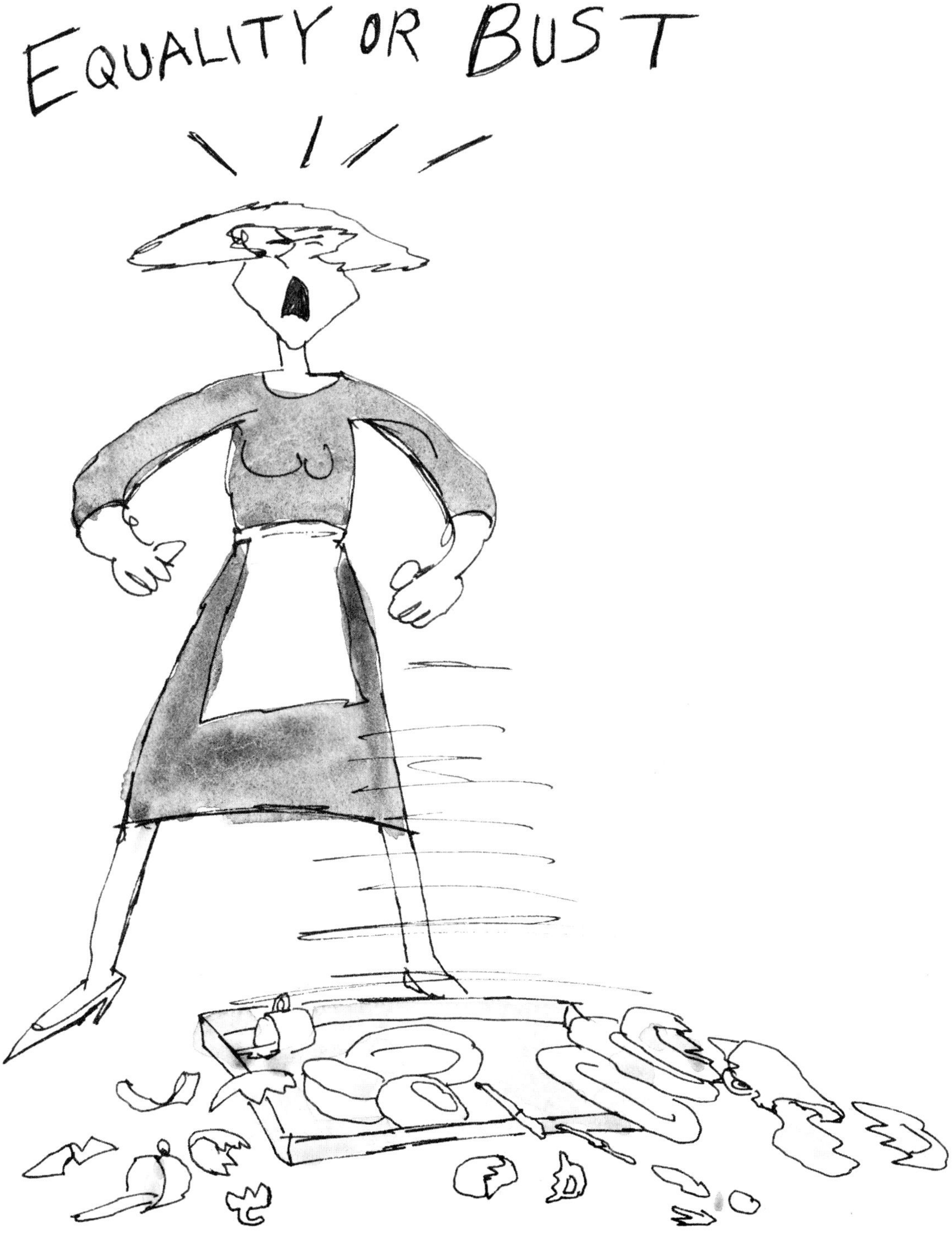
EQUALITY OR BUST

Will it never stop raining? Will Damian ever stop scrapping over Emma's Greenham Common Battle game? With twenty two missiles, two thousand soldiers and eight hundred police on his side and only seventy three women on her side, how does she keep winning?

Deidre and Zak, her skiing instructor arrived on New Year's Eve together with Topaz, Felix and Peace. Zak and Richard found they had a lot in common ie problems in being over-competitive, fear of appearing weak etc. ...Zak is going to take Richard to his men's therapy group where they support each other in learning to change. They go to Greece in September for a fortnight's relaxation and therapy about "Why too much power oppresses men".

Topaz and Felix are spending a month on a kibbutz in August and have offerred to take Emma and Damian with them. Deidre and Carole are going on a "Discover Your Potential" package tour, windsurfing off Wollongong, Karate in Crete, hang-gliding in the Himalayas, (Mike is back home so the family is financially rosy once again).

And me, well I've enrolled with the London School of Economics, so I'll be going to summer school in Cambridge, for a fortnight's "Statistics In Politics".

"Damian-how could you?.. Well you can wash them your self this time! And take Action Man out of that fairy costume."

* Emma is becoming rather manipulative, I must teach her to be more direct....

Viv Quillin was born and brought up in Derbyshire.

After ten years as a wife and mother with no pay, no time off and no promotion in sight, she was perfectly qualified for her next job.

She's been a cartoonist ever since. This is her fourth book.

that woman never gives up .

First published in Great Britain 1985
by Elm Tree Books/Hamish Hamilton Ltd
Garden House 57-59 Long Acre London WC2E 9JZ

Copyright © 1985 by Viv Quillin

British Library Cataloguing in Publication Data

Quillin, Viv
    When the chips are down who cooks the fish?
    I. English wit and humor, Pictorial
    I. Title
    741.5'942   NC1479

ISBN 0-241-11582-5

Printed and bound in Great Britain by
R. J. Acford Ltd, Chichester, West Sussex